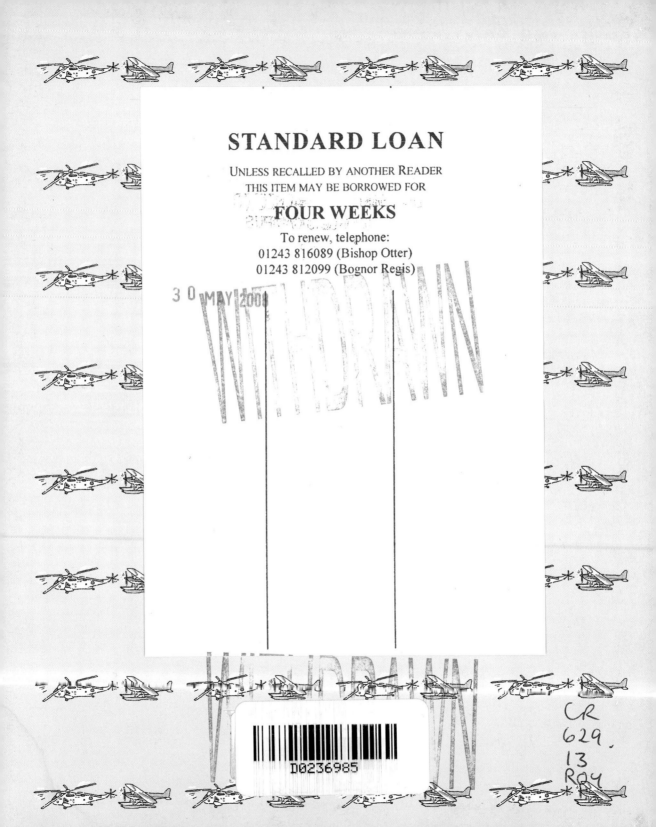

STANDARD LOAN

UNLESS RECALLED BY ANOTHER READER
THIS ITEM MAY BE BORROWED FOR

FOUR WEEKS

To renew, telephone:
01243 816089 (Bishop Otter)
01243 812099 (Bognor Regis)

A DORLING KINDERSLEY BOOK

Editor Dawn Sirett
Managing Editor Jane Yorke
Designer Karen Fielding
Senior Art Editor Mark Richards
Production Jayne Wood

Photography by Tim Ridley
Additional photography by Acorn Studios PLC, London (pages 6-7)
Illustrations by Jane Cradock-Watson and Dave Hopkins
Model makers Ted Taylor (pages 4-17 and 20-21)
and Edgar Gillingwater (pages 18-19)

Eye Openers ®

First published in Great Britain in 1992
by Dorling Kindersley Limited,
9 Henrietta Street, London WC2E 8PS

A CIP catalogue record for this book is available
from the British Library.

ISBN 0-86318-758-7

Reproduced by Colourscan, Singapore
Printed and bound in Italy by L.E.G.O., Vicenza

·EYE·OPENERS·
Planes

Written by Angela Royston

DK

DORLING KINDERSLEY
London • New York • Stuttgart

Light aircraft

Light aircraft are
small planes. They
can be used for
many jobs. This light
aircraft helps to fight forest
fires. The pilot flies low
over the fire and tells the
fire-fighters on the
ground where to
spray water.

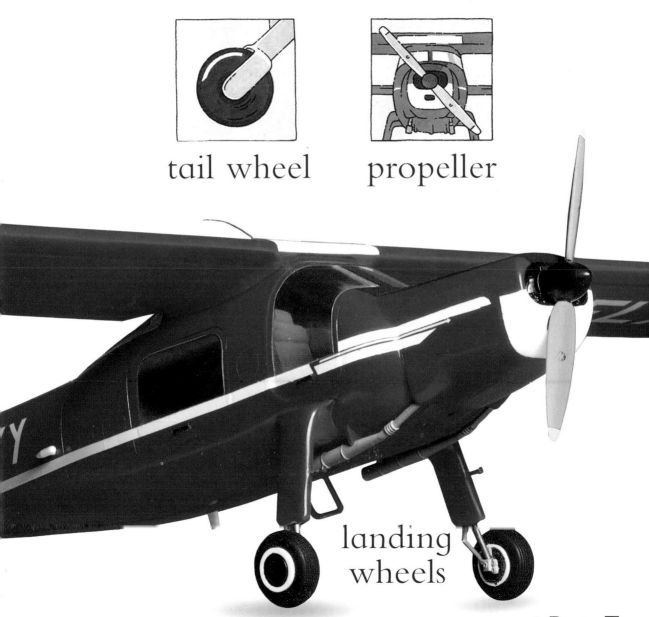

tail wheel

propeller

landing
wheels

7

Passenger plane

This plane can carry nearly 400 people. It has four big engines to make it go. People fly to different countries in passenger planes. The cabin crew look after the passengers and serve meals on board.

windows

engine

tailplane

wing

Biplane

This plane is
called a biplane
because it has two sets of
wings. It was built many years
ago. The open cockpit is very
cold and windy. The pilot has
to wear warm clothes
and goggles.

wing

rudder

propeller

wheel

Seaplane

wing

A seaplane can take off
and land on water. It has
floats instead of wheels.
Its wings are high up so
that they stay clear of the
waves. Seaplanes can
carry passengers
to small islands that
don't have runways.

HAWK XP II

14

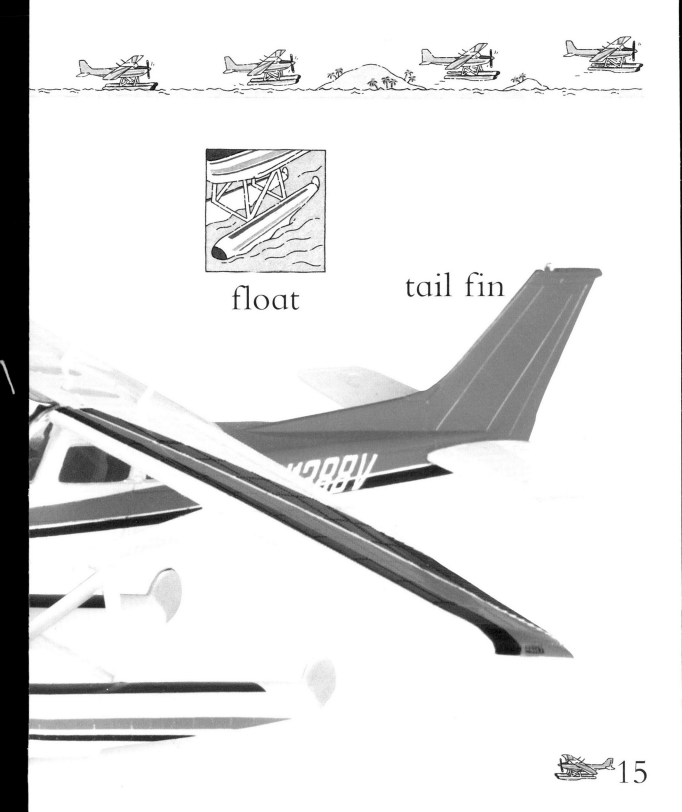

float

tail fin

Rescue helicopter

A helicopter's rotor blades spin round and lift it straight up off the ground. This helicopter is used to rescue people on mountains or at sea. It hovers in the air as people are winched up to safety.

XZ597

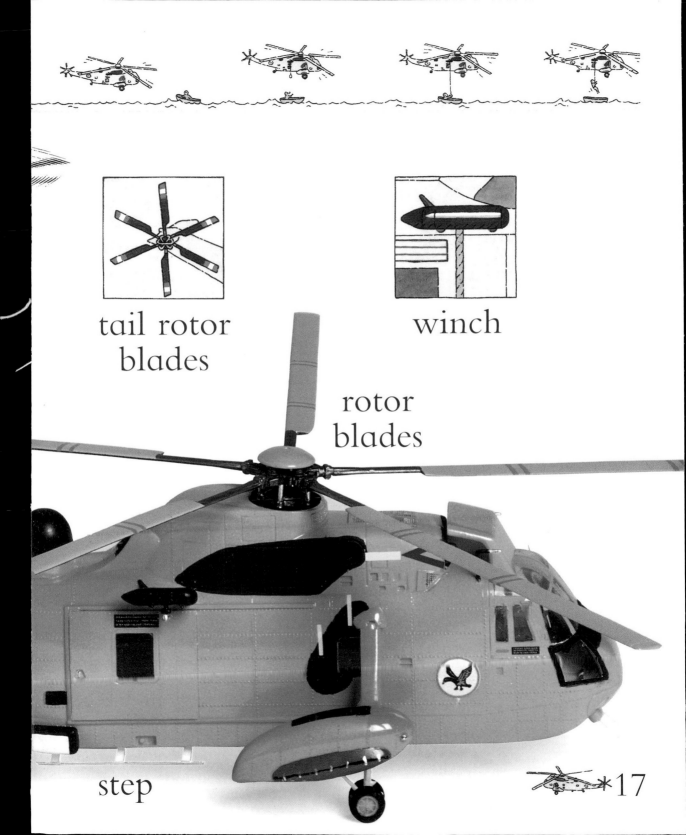

tail rotor
blades

winch

rotor
blades

step

Glider

rudder

KI

A glider's long wings help it
to fly. It has no engine, so a small
plane tows it into the sky. The glider
pilot pulls a lever to release the
tow cable. Then the glider
flies slowly back to
the ground.

18

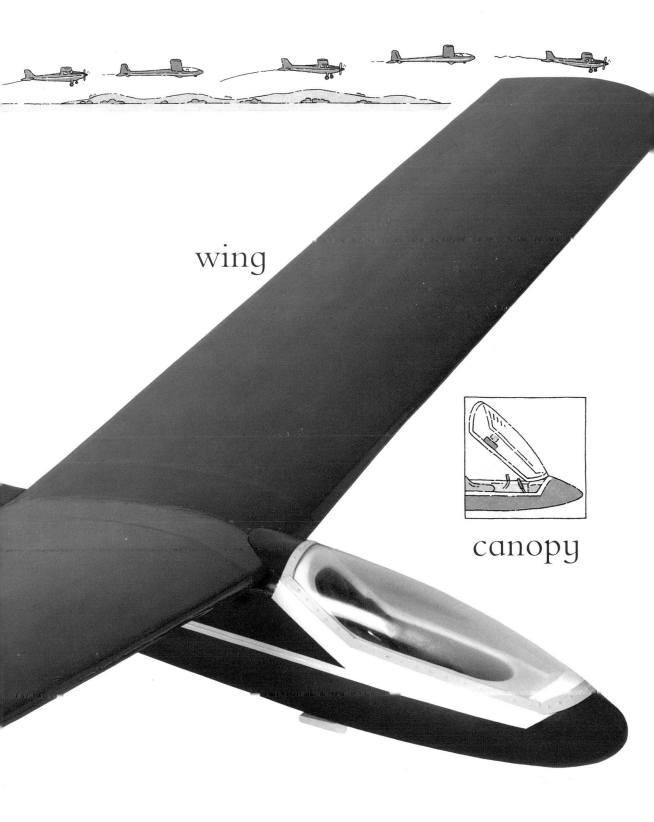

wing

canopy

Concorde

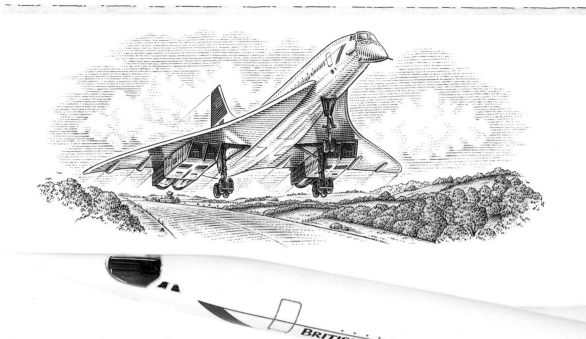

Concorde is the fastest passenger plane in the world. It can fly faster than the speed of sound. Its swept-back wings help it to speed through the air. The nose tilts down when the plane takes off or lands. This gives the pilot a clear view of the runway.

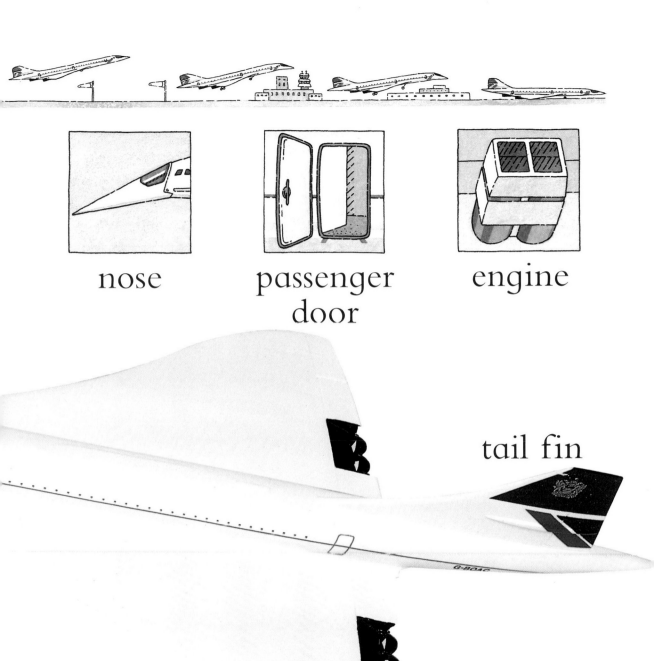

nose

passenger
door

engine

tail fin

wing

21

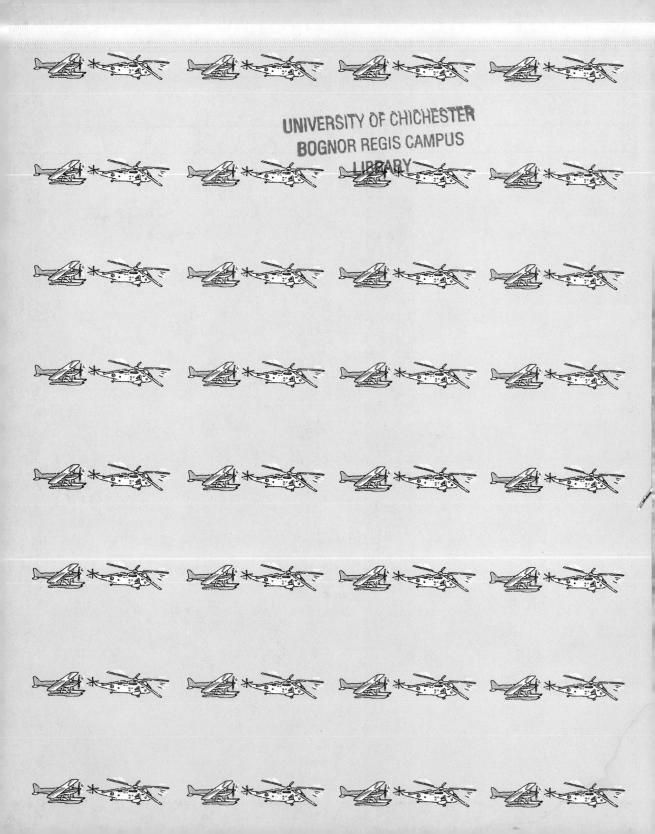